Footl
Smasn

Contents

Titles in the Runway series

Badger Publishing Limited
15 Wedgwood Gate, Pin Green Industrial Estate,
Stevenage, Hertfordshire SG1 4SU
Telephone: 01438 356907. Fax: 01438 747015
www.badger-publishing.co.uk
enquiries@badger-publishing.co.uk

Football Smash ISBN 978 1 84691 375 4

Text © Jonny Zucker, David Orme 2008
Complete work © Badger Publishing Limited 2008

Publisher: David Jamieson
Commissioning Editor: Carrie Lewis
Design: Fiona Grant
Illustration: Seb Camagajevac; Anthony Williams

Football
Smash

Written by Jonny Zucker
Illustrated by Seb Camagajevac

Taz liked to play outside.
He liked to kick his football.
Taz loved football.
His best team were Arsenal.

Taz kicked his ball against the wall.
It came back to him.
He kicked it again.
It hit the wall and came back.

Then Taz kicked the ball too high
It went up and up.
It went over the wall.

Then Taz heard a sound.
He looked round.
The ball had come back over the wall!

There must be a boy on the other side.
Who was he?
What was his name?
Did he like Arsenal too?

Taz ran to the wall.
"Thank you!" he called.
But there was no answer.

Taz kicked the ball over the wall again.
A few seconds later, the ball came back.

"Who are you?" Taz called.
But there was no answer.

The next day, Taz kicked the ball over the wall.
Seconds later, the ball came back.
It was that boy again.
Maybe he did like Arsenal!

Taz went to Mr Green.
"Who lives on the other side of the wall?"
he asked.

"Sorry," said Mr Green, "I don't know."

The next day, Dad got Taz up early.
"We are going today," said Dad.

"Where are we going?" asked Taz.

"To a new home," said Dad.

Taz said goobye to Mr Green.

"Good luck Taz," said Mr Green.

"Thank you," said Taz.

Taz and Dad walked past a gate.
Taz saw the house next door.
He saw a football being kicked in the air.

"Wait a second, Dad," said Taz.

There was the person who had kicked his ball back.
It was not a boy.
It was a girl.
She was wearing a football shirt.
But it wasn't an Arsenal shirt – it was a Tottenham shirt!

Keep on Running

Written by David Orme
Illustrated by Anthony Williams

Baz saw a big guy steal a bag
He ran after him to try and get the bag
back.

Baz nearly caught up with the thief.
Two police officers were coming the other
way.
They saw the guy with the bag.
They saw Baz running after him.

The policeman grabbed the thief.
The thief tried to run off,
so the policeman used his handcuffs.

The policewoman stopped Baz.

I *want to talk to you!*

Baz thought he was in trouble.
He turned to run.

He didn't see the person behind
He tripped over the shopping bag.

The policewoman said it was okay.

The policewoman told Baz she was a coach at the local sports club.

You are a great runner. If you want to take up running, I can help you.

Baz had never thought about running.
A week later, he joined the sports club.
Everyone there thought Baz was brilliant
at running.

Baz started training.
He was good, but it was hard work.
Sometimes he wanted to give up.

The coach really helped Baz.
He learnt lots about running.
He learnt lots about keeping really fit.

Baz stuck with it.
He started taking part in races.
He started winning. That felt great!

Soon, Baz was good enough to go to big competitions.
He was one of the fastest runners in the world.

Until one day…

Vocabulary

Football Smash

outside
kicked
football
against
sound
Arsenal
seconds
answer
person
Tottenham

Keep on Running

guy
thief
running
caught up
officers
handcuffs
thought
coach
brilliant
training

winning
competitions
fastest

⟫⟫ Story questions

Football Smash

Does Taz love Tottenham Football Club?
Who does Taz think is behind the wall?
Is Taz pleased when he finds out who it really is?
Can you think of any other sporting 'rivals'?

Keep on Running

Why does Baz chase the big guy?
Who talks to Baz about being a runner?
Was Baz the fastest runner straight away?
What does, 'Baz takes the gold', mean?